# Franklin Hanson

# EASY GROWTH IN READING

## PRIMER LEVEL TWO

# FUN IN STORY

BY

### GERTRUDE HILDRETH
TEACHERS COLLEGE, COLUMBIA UNIVERSITY

### ALLIE LOU FELTON     MABEL J. HENDERSON
### ALICE MEIGHEN

ILLUSTRATED BY
### ERICK BERRY AND FREDERICK T. CHAPMAN

## THE JOHN C. WINSTON COMPANY

# COLLABORATING EDITORS

**GRACE A. ALLEN**
Assistant Director of Training
State Teachers College
Buffalo, New York

**JOY MUCHMORE LACEY**
Professor of Education
Indiana State Teachers College
Terre Haute, Indiana

**EULA A. JOHNSTON**
Elementary Supervisor
Hamilton County
Chattanooga, Tennessee

**ETHEL MALTBY GEHRES**
Author of Primary Readers
Philadelphia, Pennsylvania

P-7-41

## Stories for You

# THREE LITTLE RABBITS

# Three Little Rabbits

One little rabbit!
Two little rabbits!
Three little rabbits!
They had a good home.
But they did not stay at home.

The little rabbits ran away.
One wanted to walk.
One wanted to run.
One wanted to play.
They wanted to have
a good time.

One little rabbit said,
"Come, let us walk."
One little rabbit said,
"Come, let us run."
One little rabbit said,
"Oh! Let us stay here.
Let us stay here and play."

And they did.

4

One little rabbit said,
"Stop! What was that?
What did I see?"
One little rabbit said,
"Oh! What was that?"
One little rabbit said,
"What did I see?
Oh! Let us run!
Let us run away.
Let us run home."

5

They saw a big tiger.

They looked and looked at him.

They wanted to run.

They wanted to get away.

They wanted Mother Rabbit.

The tiger said,
"Stay, little rabbits!
One little rabbit!
Two little rabbits!
Three little rabbits!
I like little rabbits.
Come, little rabbits.
Look at my eyes.
Look at my eyes."

The little rabbits looked.

They saw two big eyes.

They wanted to run.

They wanted to get away.

The tiger said,

"Now, I am going to eat you.

I am going to eat you up!"

They looked and looked at him.

What did they do?

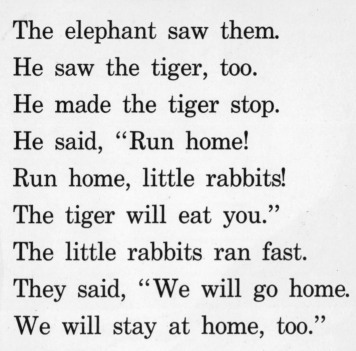

The elephant saw them.
He saw the tiger, too.
He made the tiger stop.
He said, "Run home!
Run home, little rabbits!
The tiger will eat you."
The little rabbits ran fast.
They said, "We will go home.
We will stay at home, too."

And they did!
See them in bed.

# BUSHY TAIL
## and
# BOB TAIL

13

## Bushy Tail and Bob Tail

Bushy Tail was a squirrel.
He had a house in a tree.
He was happy.

14

Bob Tail was a rabbit.
He had a house in the ground.
He was not happy.

Bob Tail was not happy.
He wanted to live in a tree.
He wanted a house in a tree.
He said, "I live in the ground.
I do not like the ground.
I do not like my house.
I want to live in a tree."

Bob Tail went for a walk.
He was crying.
Bushy Tail saw him crying.
Bushy Tail said, "Stop!
Stop crying, Bob Tail!
Can I help you?"
Bob Tail said, "Oh! Oh!
I do not like the ground.
I want to live in a tree."

Bushy Tail said, "Oh, my!
I live up in a tree.
You can live with me."
Bob Tail said, "Thank you!
Thank you, Bushy Tail.
I will go with you now."

And away they went.

They saw a big tree.
Bushy Tail said, "Stop!
This is where I live.
My house is in this tree.
Climb up to my house.
Climb up and live with me."

And up went Bushy Tail.

Bob Tail looked up.
Bushy Tail looked down.
Bob Tail was crying.
Bushy Tail saw him crying.
Bushy Tail said, "Stop crying!
Crying will not help you.
Climb! Climb the tree.
Come up to my house."

Bob Tail looked at Bushy Tail.
He wanted to climb the tree.
He said, "I want to come up.
I want to live with you."
Bushy Tail said, "Oh, climb!
Climb, Bob Tail, climb!
There is a dog!
A dog! A dog!"

What did Bob Tail do?

Bob Tail ran fast.

The dog ran fast, too.

He ran after Bob Tail.

Bob Tail said, "Oh! Oh!

The dog will catch me!

I want to hide!

I want to hide!"

He ran and ran and ran.
He saw a house in the ground.
He said, "Oh! I can hide here!
The dog can not get in here."

And in he ran.

He looked around at the house.
He said, "What a pretty house!
Oh, this is my house!
I like my pretty house.
I do not want to live in a tree.
A house in the ground!
A house in the ground!
A house in the ground for me!"

# THREE LITTLE HENS
## ON THE FARM

White Hen

Black Hen

Red Hen

# Three Little Hens on the Farm

The three hens went for a walk.
They wanted to find three nests.
They looked and they looked.
White Hen said, "I see a nest."
Black Hen said, "I see a nest."
Red Hen said, "I see a nest."

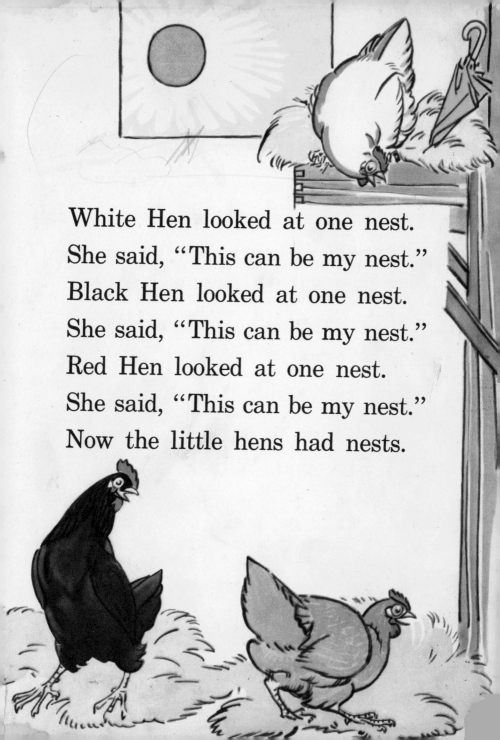

White Hen looked at one nest.
She said, "This can be my nest."
Black Hen looked at one nest.
She said, "This can be my nest."
Red Hen looked at one nest.
She said, "This can be my nest."
Now the little hens had nests.

White Hen sat on one nest.

Black Hen sat on one nest.

Red Hen sat on one nest.

White Hen said, "Cluck, cluck.

I have eggs in my nest."

Black Hen said, "Cluck, cluck.

I have eggs in my nest."

Red Hen said, "Cluck, cluck.

I have eggs in my nest."

White Hen sat on the eggs.
She said, "Cluck, cluck.
I will have white chicks."
Black Hen sat on the eggs.
She said, "Cluck, cluck.
I will have black chicks."
Red Hen sat on the eggs.
She said, "Cluck, cluck.
I will have red chicks."

The little hens sat and sat.
White Hen said, "Cluck, cluck."
White Hen wanted white chicks.
Black Hen said, "Cluck, cluck."
Black Hen wanted black chicks.
Red Hen said, "Cluck, cluck."
Red Hen wanted red chicks.

A little chick went, "Peep."

White Hen said, "Cluck, cluck.

My little chicks will be white."

A little chick went, "Peep."

Black Hen said, "Cluck, cluck.

My little chicks will be black."

A little chick went, "Peep."

Red Hen said, "Cluck, cluck.

My little chicks will be red."

White Hen said, "Cluck, cluck.
Now I will look at my chicks."
Black Hen said, "Cluck, cluck.
Now I will look at my chicks."
Red Hen said, "Cluck, cluck.
Now I will look at my chicks."

They looked and they looked.
And what did they see?
Not little white chicks!
Not little black chicks!
Not little red chicks!

But—little yellow chicks!
Peep, peep, peep!

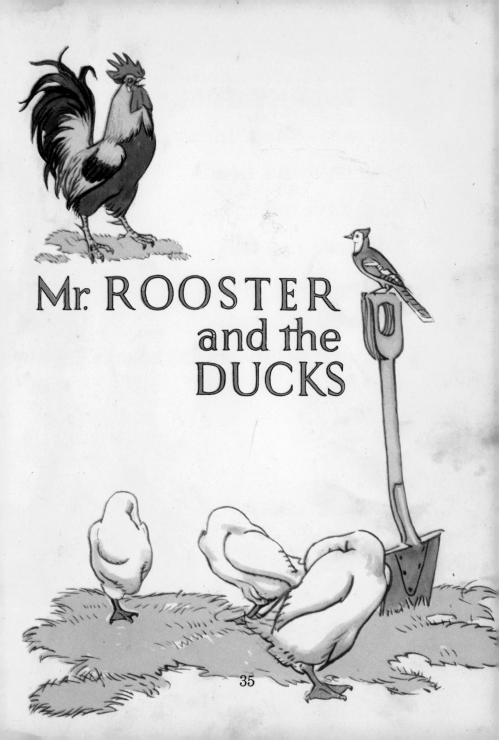

# Mr. ROOSTER
## and the
## DUCKS

# Mr. Rooster and the Ducks

Mr. Rooster saw the ducks.

He said, "You funny ducks!

You have no heads.

You have no eyes.

You can not talk.

You can not see.

You can not eat.

You are funny, funny ducks."

Mr. Rooster said,

"I want the hens to see you.

I will go and find them.

I will find Little Red Hen.

I will find Little Black Hen.

I will find Little White Hen.

I want them to see you."

Red Hen sat on a nest.

Black Hen sat on a nest.

White Hen sat on a nest.

Mr. Rooster ran to them.

He said, "Oh, little hens!

Come with me!

Come and see the funny ducks!"

The little hens said,
"We will go.
We will go with you."
And they went.
Little Red Hen!
Little Black Hen!
Little White Hen!
They went with Mr. Rooster.

"Oh! Oh!" said the little hens.
"They are funny ducks.
They have no heads.
They have no eyes.
They have just one leg!
They have just one leg!
They can not walk.
They are funny, funny ducks."

Little Red Hen said,
"I want the rabbit to see them."
Little Black Hen said,
"We will find the rabbit."
Little White Hen said,
"He will want to see
the funny, funny ducks."

And away they went
to find White Rabbit.

White Rabbit was fast asleep.
The little hens said,
"Come, White Rabbit!
Come with us!
Come and see
the funny, funny ducks!"
White Rabbit sat up.
He said, "Funny ducks!
Where are they?
I want to see them.
I will go with you."

White Rabbit said,
"What funny ducks!
They have no heads.
They have no eyes.
They have just one leg.
They can not walk."

Mr. Rooster said,

"Here comes the dog.

He will want to see them.

He will want to see
the funny ducks.

Look, Big Dog!

Look at the funny ducks!

They have no heads.

They have just one leg."

The dog looked at them.
The hens looked at them.
The rabbit looked at them.
The dog said, "Bow-wow,
bow-wow, bow-wow!"

Out came the heads.
Down went the legs.
"Quack, quack, quack, quack,"
said the ducks.
And away they ran
on two legs.

# LITTLE ELEPHANT
## and the
## WATER

# Little Elephant and the Water

Little Elephant went
down to the water.
He looked in the water.
He said, "What do I see?"
He looked
and looked
and looked.

And he fell in!

Little Elephant was crying.

Baby Tiger heard him crying.

Baby Tiger came to the water.

He said, "Oh, Baby Elephant!

I heard you crying!

Can I help you?

Can I help you?"

49

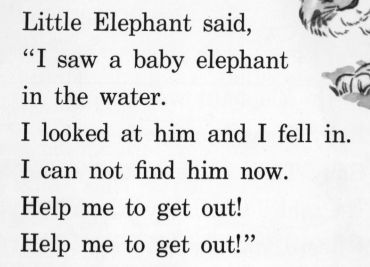

Little Elephant said,
"I saw a baby elephant
in the water.
I looked at him and I fell in.
I can not find him now.
Help me to get out!
Help me to get out!"

Baby Tiger said,
"I will help you.
Catch my tail.
I will pull you out."

Baby Elephant said,
"I will catch your tail.
You can pull me out.
Pull, Baby Tiger, pull!"

But—Baby Tiger fell in, too.

Little Elephant was crying.

Baby Tiger was crying.

Mr. Monkey heard them crying.

He came to the water.

He said, "Oh, Little Elephant!

Oh, Baby Tiger!

I heard you crying!

Can I help you?

Can I help you?"

The elephant and the tiger said,

"Help us to get out!

Help us to get out!

We fell in.

We want to get out!"

Mr. Monkey said,

"I will help you.

I will help you to get out.

Catch my tail.

I will pull you out."

The tiger said,
"I will catch your tail.
The elephant can catch my tail.
And you can pull us out."
The elephant said,
"You can pull us out.
Pull, Mr. Monkey!
Pull! Pull us out!"

But—Mr. Monkey fell in, too.

The elephant was crying.

The tiger was crying.

The monkey was crying.

They did not like the water.

Three little rabbits saw them.

They saw the elephant.

They saw the tiger.

They saw the monkey.

They saw them in the water.

The elephant said,
"Here are the little rabbits.
They will help us.
They will pull us out."
The tiger said,
"Look at the rabbits' tails.
Rabbits can not help us."

The little rabbits said,
"Stop crying, Little Elephant.
Stop crying, Baby Tiger.
Stop crying, Mr. Monkey.
We can help you.
Little Elephant, you catch
Baby Tiger's tail.
Baby Tiger, you catch
Mr. Monkey's tail.
Now —

We can not pull you out.
But—you can walk out."

And that is just what they did.

# BIG BEAR'S
# SACK

# Big Bear's Sack

Tramp, tramp, tramp.
Big Bear was going
down to the water.
He had a big sack.
He went tramp, tramp, tramp.

Big Bear looked up.

He said, "It is going to rain."

Bushy Tail heard Big Bear.

He saw Big Bear's sack.

He said, "Oh, Big Bear!

What is in your sack?"

Big Bear said,

"Something for you to find out.

Something for you to find out."

Bushy Tail said,
"I will find out.
I will go with you.
I will find out
what is in your sack."
Big Bear said, "You may go.
But do not get near my sack."

And down to the water they went.

Tramp, tramp, tramp
went Big Bear.
Tippety, tip-tip,
tippety, tip-tip
went Bushy Tail.

63

Big Bear looked up.

He said, "It is going to rain."

Bob Tail heard Big Bear.

He saw Big Bear's sack.

He said, "Oh, Big Bear!

What is in your sack?"

Big Bear said,

"Something for you to find out.

Something for you to find out."

Bob Tail said,
"I will find out.
I will go with you.
I will find out
what is in your sack."
Big Bear said, "You may go.
But do not get near my sack."

And down to the water they went.

Tramp, tramp, tramp
went Big Bear.
Tippety, tip-tip,
tippety, tip-tip
went Bushy Tail.
Hoppety, hop, hop,
hoppety, hop, hop
went Bob Tail.

Big Bear looked up.

He said, "It is going to rain."

Little Monkey heard Big Bear.

He saw Big Bear's sack.

He said, "Oh, Big Bear!

What is in your sack?"

Big Bear said,

"Something for you to find out.

Something for you to find out."

Little Monkey said,
"I will find out.
I will go with you.
I will find out
what is in your sack."
Big Bear said, "You may go.
But do not get near my sack."

And down to the water they went.

Tramp, tramp, tramp
went Big Bear.
Tippety, tip-tip,
tippety, tip-tip
went Bushy Tail.
Hoppety, hop, hop,
hoppety, hop, hop
went Bob Tail.
Tip-tip, tip-tip, tip-tip
went Little Monkey.

Big Bear looked up.
He said, "It is going to rain."
Yellow Tiger heard Big Bear.
He saw Big Bear's sack.
He said, "Oh, Big Bear!
What is in your sack?"
Big Bear said,
"Something for you to find out.
Something for you to find out."

Yellow Tiger said,
"I will find out.
I will go with you.
I will find out
what is in your sack."
Big Bear said, "You may go.
But do not get near my sack."

And down to the water they went.

71

Tramp, tramp, tramp
went Big Bear.
Tippety, tip-tip
went Bushy Tail.
Hoppety, hop, hop
went Bob Tail.
Tip-tip, tip-tip, tip-tip
went Little Monkey.
Creep, creep, creep
went Yellow Tiger.

Big Bear looked all around.
He said, "It is going to rain.
But here we are at the water.
Now, you may see
what is in my sack.
Come near! Come near!"

The sack fell to the ground.

# Crack! Boom! Crack!

Yellow Tiger did not look.
Little Monkey did not look.
Bob Tail did not look.
Bushy Tail did not look.
They did not stop to see
what was in the sack.

A turtle was in the sack.
He said, "Thank you, Big Bear.
I am happy to be at home."
Big Bear said, "Now—
Yellow Tiger can see a turtle.
Little Monkey can see a turtle.
Bob Tail can see a turtle.
Bushy Tail can see a turtle.

But where are they?"

75

# TOY FAIRY'S PARTY

# Toy Fairy's Party

Toy Fairy looked around.
She said, "The toys are asleep.
The little toy duck is asleep.
The little toy lamb is asleep.
The little toy drum is asleep.
The toy soldiers are asleep.
Jack has played with them.
They have played and played.
What fun they have had!"

Toy Fairy said,
"Wake up! Wake up, toys!
Wake up, little soldiers!
Wake up, toy drum!
Wake up, toy dog!
Wake up and come to my party!"

The toys looked at the fairy.
One toy soldier said,
"Oh! Toy Fairy!
We are happy to see you.
We wanted you to come.
We wanted to have a party."
And down they came.
Red soldiers and blue soldiers!
One, two! One, two! One, two!
Down they came to the party.

The toy drum said,
"Boom! Boom! Boom!
Where are you going, soldiers?
I want to go, too."
One soldier said,
"Come, little red drum.
Come with us.
We are going to a party.
It is Toy Fairy's party."

The toy dog said,

"Bow-wow, bow-wow!"

The toy duck said,

"Quack, quack, quack!

Where are you going?

We want to go, too.

We want to go to the party."

Around and around they went.
The toy drum said, "Boom! Boom!"
The toy soldiers said,
"One, two! One, two! One, two!"
The toy dog said, "Bow-wow!"
The toy duck said, "Quack!"
What a good time they had
at Toy Fairy's party!

The little drum said,
"Boom! Boom! Boom!
I am happy! I am happy!
Jack likes me the best.
He plays with me.
He likes to hear me.
Boom! Boom! Boom!"

"Oh! Oh!" said the little dog.
"Jack likes me the best.
He likes to hear me.
Bow-wow, bow-wow!"
"Quack, quack, quack!"
said the little toy duck.
"He likes me the best!
He likes me the best!"

Toy Fairy heard a little voice.
She said, "What is that?
What is that?
What do I hear?"
A little voice said,
"Let me out! Let me out!
I want to come to the party.
I want to come to the party."

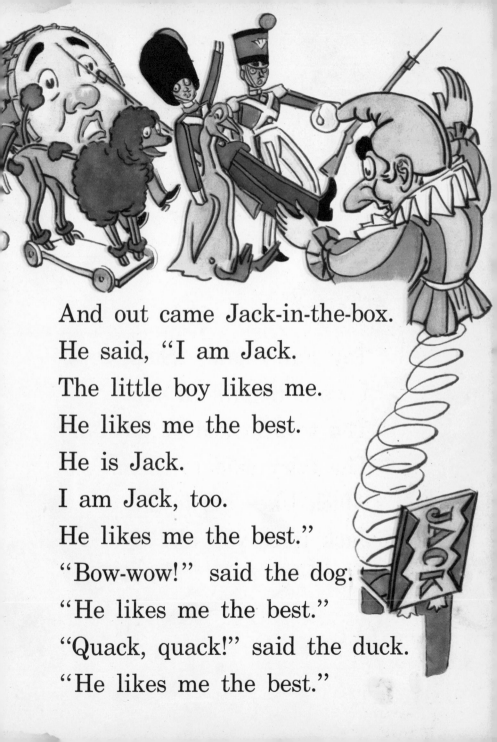

And out came Jack-in-the-box.

He said, "I am Jack.

The little boy likes me.

He likes me the best.

He is Jack.

I am Jack, too.

He likes me the best."

"Bow-wow!" said the dog.

"He likes me the best."

"Quack, quack!" said the duck.

"He likes me the best."

Toy Fairy said, "Stop, toys!
I want to talk to you."
The toys looked at the fairy.
The fairy said to them.
"Jack likes his toys.
Jack likes you all."

This made the toys happy.
They said, "Thank you!
Thank you, Toy Fairy!
Thank you for our party."
Toy Fairy said, "Good-by."

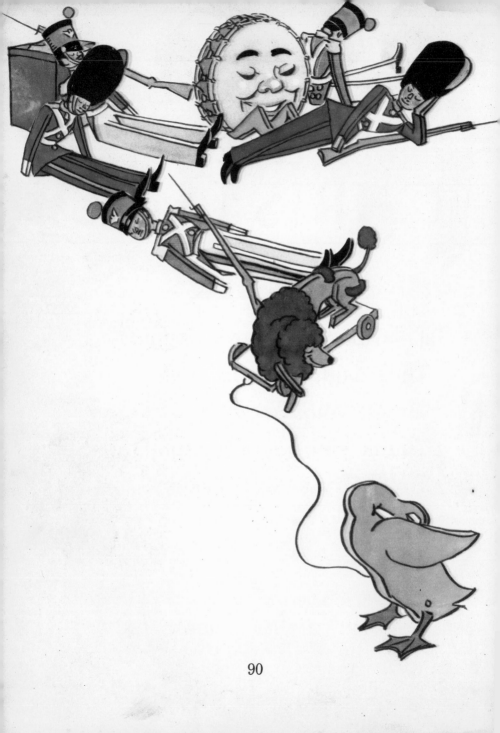

# HALLOWEEN and CHRISTMAS

OCTOBER 3 1

DECEMBER 25

## Yellow Pumpkin and Black Pussy

"I wish! I wish!"
said Yellow Pumpkin.
"I wish I had a home.
I want to live
with a happy little boy.
I want to be a jack-o'-lantern.
I want to have fun with him
on Halloween."

92

Black Pussy said,
"I wish! I wish!
I wish I had a home, too.
I want to live with
a good little girl.
She will feed me.
I want to find a home.
I want to find
a good little girl."

Yellow Pumpkin said,
"Let us go and find
a happy little boy.
Let us go and find
a good little girl."
Black Pussy said,
"It is cold now.
We want a home.
Come, let us go!"

94

They went on and on.
They saw a cow.
Yellow Pumpkin said,
"Mrs. Cow, we want a home.
I want to find
a happy little boy.
I want to be
his jack-o'-lantern.
Black Pussy wants to find
a good little girl."

Mrs. Cow said, "Come with me.
Come and live with me."
Black Pussy said, "Do not go!
Mrs. Cow will eat you.
You can not live with a cow."
Yellow Pumpkin looked
at Mrs. Cow.
He said, "Thank you, Mrs. Cow!
I guess we will go on."

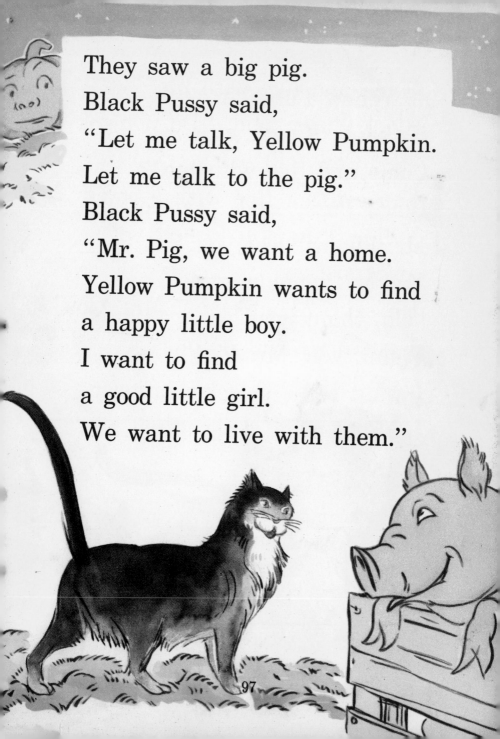

They saw a big pig.
Black Pussy said,
"Let me talk, Yellow Pumpkin.
Let me talk to the pig."
Black Pussy said,
"Mr. Pig, we want a home.
Yellow Pumpkin wants to find
a happy little boy.
I want to find
a good little girl.
We want to live with them."

Mr. Pig looked
at Yellow Pumpkin.
He said, "Come with me.
Come and live with me."
Black Pussy said, "Do not go!
Mr. Pig will eat you."
Yellow Pumpkin said,
"Oh, thank you!
Thank you, Mr. Pig!
I want to be a jack-o'-lantern.
I do not want a pig to eat me."

98

They heard a little voice.
The little voice said,
"Where are you going,
Yellow Pumpkin?
Where are you going,
Black Pussy?"
They looked for the voice,
and what did they see?

A fairy! A fairy!
Yellow Pumpkin said,
"Oh! Fairy! Fairy!
We want to find a home.
Black Pussy wants to find
a good little girl.
I want to find
a happy little boy.
I want to be
his jack-o'-lantern.
Will you help us?"

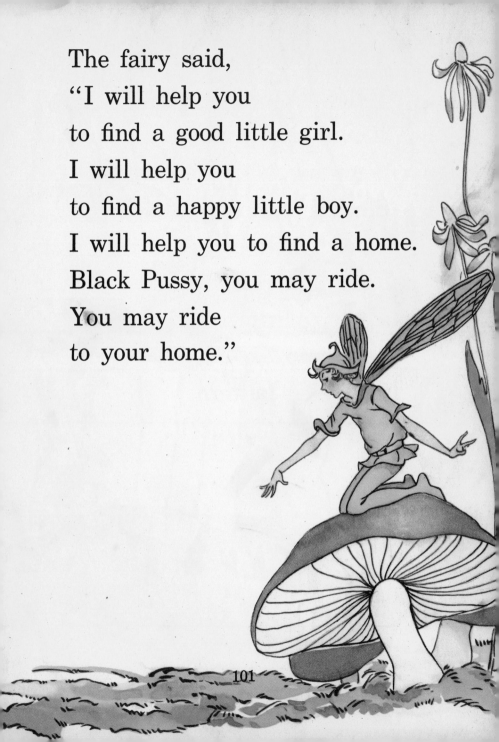

The fairy said,
"I will help you
to find a good little girl.
I will help you
to find a happy little boy.
I will help you to find a home.
Black Pussy, you may ride.
You may ride
to your home."

# A CHRISTMAS STORY

# Santa Claus!

# Toys for Boys and Girls

Christmas had come.
Snow was on the ground.
Santa Claus looked at the toys.
Balls! Trains! Dolls!
Mrs. Santa looked at the toys.
Mrs. Santa said, "I am happy.
Christmas makes me happy."

Santa Claus said, "I am happy.
Christmas makes me happy, too.
I want to see the little boys.
I want to see the little girls.
I want to make them happy."

Mrs. Santa said, "Good-by!
What fun you will have!
The boys and girls like toys.
They will be happy."

Bob Tail saw Santa Claus.

He said, "Stop, Santa Claus!

Where are you going?

I want to see you.

My baby rabbits want to see you.

They want you to come.

They want to see you."

Santa Claus looked at Bob Tail.

He said, "I have toys.

Toys are for boys and girls.

I can not come to see you now."

Bob Tail looked at Santa Claus.

He went away crying.

Santa Claus looked at Bob Tail.

He said, "What can I do?

What can I do?"

Bushy Tail saw Santa Claus.
He said, "Stop, Santa Claus!
Where are you going?
I want to see you.
My baby squirrels
want to see you.
They want you to come."

Santa Claus looked
at Bushy Tail.
He said, "I have toys.
Toys are for boys and girls.
I can not come to see you now."
Bushy Tail went away crying.
Santa Claus said,
"Oh, what can I do?"

114

115

Santa Claus said,

"Now I am happy.

I have toys for boys and girls.

Airplanes! Boats! Dolls!

I have something for rabbits.

I have something for squirrels.

I can make them happy, too."

Mrs. Santa said,

"Good-by! Good-by!"

Santa Claus came to a big tree.
He said, "Oh! Oh!
Here is Bushy Tail's home.
Bushy Tail lives in a tree.
He wanted me to come.
I have something
for his baby squirrels.
This will make them happy."

Santa Claus looked
at the ground.
He said, "Oh! Oh!
Here is Bob Tail's home.
Bob Tail lives in the ground.
He wanted me to come.
I have something
for his baby rabbits.
This will make them happy."

119

Mrs. Santa said,

"You look happy."

Santa Claus said, "I am happy.

The boys and girls are happy.

The little rabbits are happy.

The squirrels are happy.

And I am happy, too."

# WORD LIST

The following list contains the 63 new words introduced in Primer Level Two. All of the words presented in Primer Level One (except frog, pony, balloon, man, Anne, Jean) are repeated in this Primer Level Two. No page has more than two new words.

Because of the unusual control of vocabulary the book can be read with ease as shown by:

74 pages with 0 new words
31 pages with 1 new word
16 pages with 2 new words

| # | word | # | word | # | word | # | word |
|---|------|---|------|---|------|---|------|
| 1 | rabbit | 22 | | 41 | | 61 | rain |
| 2 | stay | 23 | | 42 | asleep | | something |
| 3 | | 24 | | 43 | | 62 | near |
| 4 | let | 25 | black | 44 | | 63 | Tippety |
| 5 | that | | white | 45 | | | tip-tip |
| 6 | tiger | 26 | nest | 46 | came | 64 | |
| 7 | eyes | 27 | | 47 | water | 65 | |
| 8 | eat | 28 | sat | 48 | fell | 66 | Hoppety |
| 9 | | | eggs | | | | hop |
| 10 | | 29 | | 49 | heard | 67 | |
| 11 | elephant | 30 | | 50 | | 68 | |
| 12 | | 31 | peep | 51 | your | 69 | |
| 13 | Bushy | 32 | | | pull | 70 | |
| | Tail | 33 | | 52 | | 71 | |
| 14 | squirrel | 34 | | 53 | | 72 | creep |
| | tree | 35 | Mr. | 54 | | 73 | |
| 15 | ground | | Rooster | 55 | | 74 | crack |
| 16 | | 36 | head | 56 | | | boom |
| 17 | crying | | no | 57 | | 75 | turtle |
| 18 | | 37 | | 58 | | 76 | |
| 19 | climb | 38 | | 59 | bear | 77 | Fairy |
| 20 | | 39 | | | sack | 78 | drum |
| 21 | dog | 40 | just | 60 | tramp | | soldier |
| | | | leg | | | | |

| | | | | | | |
|---|---|---|---|---|---|---|
| 79 | wake | 89 | | 99 | | 110 |
| 80 | | 90 | | 100 | | 111 |
| 81 | | 91 | | 101 | | 112 |
| 82 | | 92 | pussy | 102 | | 113 |
| 83 | | | wish | 103 | | 114 |
| 84 | best | 93 | | 104 | | 115 |
| | hear | 94 | | 105 | | 116 |
| 85 | | 95 | Mrs. | 106 | Santa Claus | 117 |
| 86 | voice | 96 | | 107 | | 118 |
| 87 | Jack-in-the-box | 97 | | 108 | Santa | 119 |
| 88 | his | 98 | | 109 | | 120 |
| | | | | | | 121 |

## VOCABULARY TABLE

| Pre-Primer Level One | Pre-Primer Level Two | Pre-Primer Level Three | Primer Level One | Primer Level Two |
|---|---|---|---|---|
| Basic Words    52 | 52 | 52 | 52 | 46 |
| | New Words   15 | 5 | 15 | 10 |
| | 67 | | | |
| | | New Words   8 | 8 | 4 |
| | | 65 | | |
| | | | New Words   81 | 75 |
| | | | 156 | |
| | | | | New Words   63 |
| | | | | 198 |

This table shows the cumulative and repetitive vocabulary of each book in the series through Primer, Level Two. Reading down the steps of the table the new words of each book are shown. Reading across the table the repetition of words is shown.   For example: All 52 words introduced in Pre-Primer, Level One are repeated in Pre-Primers, Level Two and Three, and in Primer, Level One; 46 of them are repeated in Primer, Level Two, etc.

# ACKNOWLEDGMENTS

Grateful acknowledgment is made to the following authors and publishers for special permission to make adaptations from copyrighted material:

To Elise Reid Boylston for "Three Little Hens on the Farm," "Mr. Rooster and the Ducks," "Little Elephant and the Water," and "Big Bear's Sack."

For the "Three Little Rabbits" based on the picture story of the title "Three Merry Rabbits" in *The Cautious Carp* by Nicholas Radlov, and used by special arrangement with Coward McCann, Inc.

For "Yellow Pumpkin and Black Pussy" adapted from "A Halloween Story" by Elizabeth T. Dillingham from Dillingham and Emerson's *Tell It Again Stories* published by Ginn and Company.